Casper's done some pretty exciting things:

- He's been to the moon with the Apollo 16 Astronauts, who named their command module after him!

- He's working for the United Nations Children's Emergency Fund (UNICEF) to help swell the fund used for needy children around the world!

- He's joined the Boy Scouts of America, to welcome new Cub Scouts into the fold!

- He's been in the movies in many languages!

- He's in eight different comic magazines, read by over 36 million Americans each year—and by many more all over the world in many languages.

- He's on over 400 different items—clothes, food, toys, games!

- *And now—Casper's in paperback books—this is the very first time!*

Casper®

The Friendly Ghost

Ghost Stories

tempo books

GROSSET & DUNLAP

Publishers   New York

NO DOUBT ABOUT IT! IT *IS* FOLLOWING ME! IT'S KIND OF *CREEPY!*

LOOK... I *DON'T UNDERSTAND* THIS, BUT YOU *STAY* RIGHT HERE TILL I *FIND WENDY!*

SLURP!

PEEP!

HA! THE BUBBLE HIT HIM IN THE NOSE!

NOW HE'LL WANT TO DANCE!

HOW DO YOU LIKE THAT? EVERYBODY ELSE *DANCES,* LAZO *SLEEPS!*

A *FUNNY* BIRD IS THE *PELICAN*... HIS *BILL* HOLDS MORE THAN HIS *BELLY CAN!*

HEY... THAT'S AN IDEA!

KEEP YOUR *BILL* OPEN!

OKAY... LOWER AWAY!

I'M TOO GOOD NATURED!

GOT 'IM ALL?

YEP!

THEN *ON* TO THE *MOUNTAIN!*

THE END

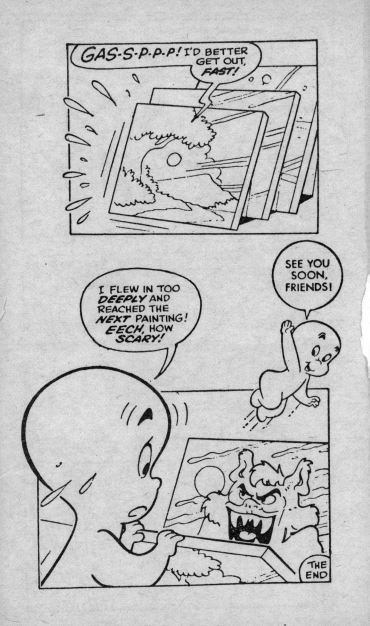

THE FRIENDLY GHOST.
Casper

IT TAKES A *LOT* TO SCARE *ME* AFTER ALL THEIR *BOOING* AT ME!

OH! THERE'S A *NICE, QUIET PAINTING* IN FRONT OF THAT *ART GALLERY!*

I'LL *DIVE IN* THERE AND *RELAX!*